Prayers That Make a Difference

by
Marjorie Soderholm

FCP

FREE CHURCH PRESS
1515 E. 66th St.
Minneapolis, MN 55423

Preface

Are you satisfied with your prayer life? You can be. Prayer can be a satisfying experience for you, not just for people of the Bible or for others you know. Nehemiah, David, Jesus, Paul, and others had the attention of God, the Creator and King of the Universe, when they prayed. You can, too. Their prayers had power; their prayers produced results; their prayers made a difference; and yours can, too!

Take heart! Even if your prayer life is empty, there is hope. God says so. "For whatsoever things were written aforetime were written for our learning, that we through patience and comfort of the Scriptures might have hope." (Romans 15:4) You can accept the comfort of the Scriptures and have hope because you can learn from the experiences of others.

God has recorded the prayers of many people in the Bible, and these were written for our learning. The lessons in this study guide are based upon some of those prayers. As you read the prayers and answer questions about them, you will be guided into praying for some of the very things for which they prayed. You will also pray about some of your own special concerns. And as you experience growth in your prayer life, you will know that you have the attention of God and that your prayers have power. And you will see results.

Now, more about the study guide:

This series of Bible studies is made up of two units; the first, of eight prayers recorded in the Bible; the other, of four such prayers.

The prayers in Unit One have been chosen because each emphasizes a different aspect of prayer such as petition, thanksgiving, confidence, or humility. This is not to say that each illustrates one of these aspects to the exclusion of the others, but by studying one emphasis in each prayer, a person can come to appreciate prayer in a broader context. One learns to realize more fully the reasons for prayer; sees the effect of prayer upon his or her life and upon the lives of others; recognizes God's response to prayer, and senses personal responsibility after God responds.

The prayers in Unit Two are included to further develop one's ability to study prayers of the Bible and to relate them personally to his or her own life. The same guide is used for all four of these prayers. After studying all four prayers with the use of this guide, a person should be able to profitably study many more prayers recorded in the Word of God.

Each unit is provided with instructions for use. These should be carefully read before beginning the studies in order that everyone may benefit. The entire series is designed so each person can study the prayer under consideration individually and then join a group for discussion.

These studies may be used for men's fellowship groups, women's meetings, mid-week Bible studies, home study groups, and adult Sunday school classes. College-age young people could also use these in Sunday school, Sunday evening studies, or mid-week studies. Instructors in Bible institutes, Bible colleges, or Christian liberal arts colleges will also find this series helpful in their Bible courses.

The two units may be studied consecutively, or Unit One and Unit Two may be studied separately. Suggestions for additional prayer studies are listed at the end of Unit Two.

For the Sunday school setting, the series may be used for a thirteen-week quarter. The twelve lessons could be used, allowing one Sunday either for introducing the series or concluding it, or by allowing one extra Sunday to be used for a lesson that demands more time.

Each person in the group should have a copy of this manual in order to benefit most from individual study, to contribute effectively to the group discussion, and to refer to later. The most valuable part of the manual to the participant will be that which is written during the personal study time alone with God.

Each person should be encouraged to share ideas with the group in order that all may grow in fellowship with each other. However, all should respect the Holy Spirit's work in an individual's life, realizing that at times some persons will not choose to share with the group what is happening in their hearts. Each one should have a concern for everyone else in the group, not just to get the Bible studies done, but to search together for what God wants to work into their lives through their meeting with Him around His Word.

As you study the prayers in this series of Bible studies, may you experience the joy of discovery in the Word of God, the realization of God's response to His people as they pray, and some vital changes in your own prayer life.

Marjorie Soderholm

Contents

UNIT ONE

UNIT TWO

unit one

This unit of Bible studies refers to eight prayers recorded in the Bible. Each study is in two parts: one part for study alone with God, and one part to talk over with others who have done the same study. To be of greatest benefit, each person in the group should write out his or her own study before gathering for discussion. The suggestions under *Let's Talk It Over with Others* are primarily for the leader, and are considered further in the section on instructions for the leader's preparation.

INSTRUCTIONS FOR THE INDIVIDUAL STUDYING THE PASSAGE

1. Pray for God's help in relating the passage to your own personal life.
2. Read the passage several times.
3. Write out your answers to the questions in *Let's Study It Alone with God* before each meeting.
4. Take your Bible and this study guide with you each time you meet with the group.

INSTRUCTIONS FOR THE LEADER

1. Study the passage first for your own life, following instructions for the individual study.
2. Then consider the suggestions in the *Let's Talk It Over with Others* section. Plan to follow the sequence of the *Let's Study It Alone with God* section, inserting a few of the suggestions from the *Let's Talk It Over with Others* section to add variety and insights to what the group members have prepared ahead of time. On occasion you may choose not to add any of the suggestions, but to follow the *Let's Study It Alone with God* section as is.
3. Determine the best way to open and close the session. You will find some suggestions for these in the *Let's Talk It Over with Others* section of each lesson.

4. Pray for each one in your group; pray that God will teach each one as he or she studies alone with Him, and as you meet together.

INSTRUCTIONS FOR THE LEADER
DURING THE DISCUSSION

1. Begin the discussion on time and end on time.
2. Usually open with prayer. If you ask someone in the group to pray, be sure to ask someone who will not feel put on the spot.
3. Guide the discussion; don't lecture.
4. Be sure the group sticks to the passage selected for this discussion. Don't let them wander all over the Bible. Guide them to see what the passage, at hand, has to say.
5. If someone comes up with a questionable or an incomplete answer, ask "Where did you see that?" or "What do the rest of you think?" or "What else in the passage helps answer this question?" This helps the group members refer to their Bibles for the answers, and it also helps them see for themselves whether or not what the person has said is correct. Be careful not to make sincere participants uncomfortable about their answers; rather, try to help them discover right answers.
6. Keep away from sidetracks and pet themes. Keep pointing the group back to what the Bible says.
7. Do not allow anyone to monopolize the discussion.
8. Give people time to think. Even though they have studied ahead of time, they need time to think of how their own study relates to the discussion. Do not be afraid of silence, and do not rob the group of its ability to participate by answering the question yourself.
9. Read the passage sometime during the session. It may be at the beginning; it may be in sections as the discussion proceeds; or it may be at the end. Sometimes ask each person to read it silently at the beginning of the session; sometimes request the group to read it in unison; at other times ask one person to read it aloud to the group; or let them listen to a cassette tape of the passage.
10. Make summary statements periodically to relate the

thoughts which the people are sharing. Avoid lecturing at the end. Just "tie up" ideas enough to leave the group satisfied that they have accomplished something by meeting together to talk it over with each other.

11. Allow some time for prayer either at the end or at appropriate places in the study.

INSTRUCTIONS FOR THE GROUP

1. Decide where to meet, whether to meet at the same place or to go to different places. If the latter, determine how to keep people informed as to the meeting place.
2. Decide how many times you will meet. Eight times are needed for the studies in Unit One. If Unit Two is added, twelve times will be needed. Some groups may want to meet twelve times and then after a break, meet again for seven times to do the additional studies suggested under *On Your Own*.
3. Decide how often to meet. Once a week will be good for must groups.
4. Determine a starting and closing time for each session. Then keep to it. It should be agreed that no one will feel obligated to wait for late-comers, and that everyone will do his best not to be a late-comer.
5. Agree to come together to learn what the Bible says, not to argue points on which members may disagree. Determine to keep the focus on what God says.
6. Be sure each person has a Bible and a copy of this study guide. Each one should bring both his Bible and the study guide to each session.
7. Agree that each person will come to the sessions with the study done. This gives every one in the group some background for the discussion.
8. Each person should keep his own study book for himself. He should feel free to share or not to share what he has written in that book. However, the more willing members are to share with each other, the more they will benefit from the discussion.
9. If the group is too large for all to take part, divide into smaller groups.

Studies in This Unit

Paul's Prayer of Petition
Ephesians 3:13-21

Let's Study It Alone With God

1. Read Paul's account of his prayer for the Ephesians in verses 13-21. Read it in three translations, and indicate here which translation you read.

2. List the requests that Paul made for the Ephesians. Explain what he was really asking for when he made each request.

   Request   **Explanation**

3. What is one of his requests that you could pray for someone you know?

   What is one that you could pray for yourself?

   What is one that you would like to have someone pray for you?

4. What words, phrases, or verses reflect Paul's confidence that God would answer his prayer?

5. How much of our prayer can God answer? Check the correct answer(s).

_____Some of it   _____All of it
_____Most of it   _____More than we pray for

6. Is it a lack of faith to be surprised when God answers your prayer far beyond what you asked? Explain.

7. What does Ephesians 1:19,20 tell us about the power that is working in us which is spoken of in Ephesians 3:20?

8. How does Ephesians 3:12 relate to this prayer of Paul? How does it encourage you?

9. What does it mean to be **rooted** and **grounded** in **love?** (v. 17)

10. Why could this prayer be called a prayer of petition?

11. Why could this prayer also be called a prayer of intercession?

12. What does this prayer reveal of Paul's attitude toward the Lord?

What does it reveal of his attitude toward those for whom he prayed?

What does it reveal of his attitude toward himself and his life purpose?

13. On the basis of this study, what is one thing in your prayer life that should be changed? What plans will you make for that change?

14. Memorize Ephesians 3:20. Check here when you have quoted the verse word-perfect, with reference before and after, to three people.

_____1   _____2   _____3

For Further Study

Indicate here questions and problems coming from this study that you would like to spend more time on later.

Let's Talk It Over With Others

To the leader: As you and your group proceed through the questions you have studied for LET'S STUDY IT ALONE WITH GOD, insert suggestions below as they fit into the sequence of the study. These will expand each group member's understanding of the passages, encourage a fellowship of learning and praying together, and provide you, as the leader, with ideas that will both keep your class on track and provide something in addition to the study they do on their own. The number in parentheses after each suggestion indicates which question in the **Let's Study It Alone with God** section it best follows. Select the suggestions that will be most meaningful to your group. Then indicate in the margin of your study which you plan to use. For instance, if you choose **B** and **D**, write a **B** in the margin after #1 and **D** after #5. These will then remind you to turn to the inserts as you proceed through the questions in **Let's Study It Alone with God.**

A. Ask each member of the group to turn to Psalm 119:18 and to pray the verse silently. (Before #1)

B. Read Ephesians 3:13-21 aloud from the translation most used by members of the group for this study. (After #1)

C. Ask if they noticed that in 3:19 Paul appears to be asking that they know something they can't know. Point out that he asks that they will know the love of Christ, and then he says such love is beyond knowledge. Explain that he is asking that they will know by experience the love of Christ beyond what they can comprehend with their minds. (After #2 or as it comes up in #2)

D. Read Ephesians 3:20 aloud several times, each time having one person read it, stressing one word, and explaining why that word was stressed. Explain that this is one kind of meditation, a way to "mull over" the Word of God. (After #5)

E. Ask them to share requests from #3 and #13 that they would like the group to pray for. Spend time praying for these. (After #13 or at the closing)

F. Choose a song from your hymnbook such as "Sweet Hour of Prayer," and relate it to Ephesians 3:13-21 by phrases, words, thoughts. Example: "And bids me at my Father's throne make all my wants and wishes known" with verse 20; He can do all the things I ask and more. (After #13)

G. Close in singing one stanza of the hymn from F above, in saying Ephesians 3:20 in unison, or by letting several who have memorized the verse say it.

David's Prayer
of Thanksgiving

I Chronicles 29:10-19

Let's Study It Alone With God

1. Read I Chronicles 29:1-9 to get the background of the prayer. What had David asked of the people?

2. Had David asked anything of the people that he had not experienced himself? Support your answer. (vv. 1-5)

3. How had the people responded to David's appeal? How did they feel about what they had done? (vv. 6-9)

4. List the things that David said about God as he prayed to Him. (vv. 10-19)

5. How does David's prayer reflect his attitude toward God?

6. Reread what David said about God. Think about who God is. In one sentence write how it makes you feel when you think about praying to a God like this.

7. What was David's attitude concerning what had been given to God?

8. What was his attitude toward life?

9. What is included in this prayer besides thanksgiving?

10. Write down a specific answer to prayer than you have had this week.

    Check here when you have thanked God for that answer.__

11. Read I Chronicles 29:20-22. How did the people, who were present while David prayed, act after the prayer?

12. What do you have that you could offer willingly to God? Will you do it? When?

13. Can you think of any specific examples in which one person's praying caused others who heard that prayer to worship God? If so, give an example.

14. Reflect on your own prayer life. On the basis of this study, name one thing that should be different in your prayer life. What will you do so that this change may be realized?

15. Memorize one or more verses of I Chronicles 29:11-14. Check here when you have quoted what you have memorized to someone else. Be sure to quote word-perfect with reference before and after.

> Verse(s) chosen_____
>
> Quoted word perfect_____

For Further Study

Indicate here questions and problems coming from this study that you would like to spend more time on later.

Let's Talk It Over With Others

To the leader: As you and your group proceed through the questions you have studied for LET'S STUDY IT ALONE WITH GOD, insert suggestions below as they fit into the sequence of the study. Again you may want to indicate in the margin of your study the suggestions you plan to use. That is, if you plan to use suggestion **B** mark a **B** in the margin after #5 in your **Let's Study It Alone with God** section. This will facilitate you in guiding your group to the suggestions you want to use in enriching your study together.

A. Ask one person to lead in prayer, including the petition of Psalm 119:18. (Before #1)

B. How do our prayers reflect our attitude toward God? Give some specific illustrations. (Examples: "Give-me" prayers, "Bless-them" prayers, lack of prayer, and lack of thanksgiving.) (After #5)

C. Consider each statement regarding God in verse 12 and show how each could affect our attitude toward our own lives if we related it to our everyday living. (After #8)

D. Do you think that the "average" Christian today considers life on earth as more permanent or more temporary than David did? Give reasons for your answer. How does this attitude toward life affect the way he gives and the way he prays? (After #8)

E. Have the group share answers that they have had to prayer. Have a time of thanksgiving with several praying to thank God again for specific answers to prayer. (After #10)

F. Evaluate the statement, "giving people are thankful people." (After #11)

G. What does God expect of His people besides their possessions? (After #12)

H. Ask which verse(s) each chose to memorize and the reason for the choice. (After #15)

I. Close by reading verses 11 and 12 in unison and/or by using this poem:

19

Lord, teach me to pray—
    Not only to ask,
    But also to praise.

Lord, teach me to praise—
    Not only by lip,
    But also by life.

Lord, teach me to live—
    Not only for self,
    But only for Thee.

Jesus' Prayer of Intercession

John 17

Let's Study It Alone With God

1. Read the chapter, noticing the following three things:

   a. What things did Jesus pray for Himself? (List specific things from verses 1-5)

   b. What did Jesus pray for His followers? (List specific things from verses 6-19)

   c. What did Jesus pray for those who would later believe on Him? (List specific things from verses 20-26)

2. In verse 4, Jesus said, "I have finished the work which thou gavest me to do." Reread the chapter and write down the things He said He had done. Give reference for each one.

3. In addition to the things Jesus did, what does chapter 17 tell about Him?

4. What are Jesus' two main concerns in verses 20-26? (One has to do with those who will believe on Him, and one with the world.)

5. What relationship do you see between John 17:23 and John 3:16?

6. What is the Christian's relationship to the world? (vv. 14-18, 21-23 especially)

7. Read John 18:1-4. What happened to Jesus shortly after He had prayed the prayer of John 17?

8. What relationship do you see between these verses: John 4:34, 17:4, and 19:30?

9. What are two things that make intercessory prayer hard for you? Reflect on those two difficulties and think of one thing you can do to overcome one of them. Write it down and then do it.

The difficulties: (1)

The action you can take to overcome one difficulty:

Check here when the action has been taken_____

10. What is one thing you can pray for each of these?

Yourself:

A Christian who is being misunderstood or mistreated:

Someone who has not acknowledged that Jesus came to die for him:

For Further Study

Indicate here questions and problems coming from this study that you would like to spend more time on later.

Let's Talk It Over With Others

To the leader: For help in using the suggestions below turn to the introductory paragraph of the **Let's Talk It Over with Others** section for the first Bible study in this book.

A. Sing as an opening prayer the song, "Open My Eyes, That I May See," or another prayer song of your choice. (Before #1)

B. Let three members of the group read their lists, one for each of the following:

What things did Jesus pray for Himself?

What did Jesus pray for His followers?

What did Jesus pray for those who would later believe on Him? (With #1)

C. What was Jesus' concern for us? (vv. 20,21) (After 1c)

D. Is Jesus' concern in verse 23 being realized in our lives? If so, how? If not, why not? (After 1c)

E. If you were going to tell someone what it means to believe on Jesus, what would you say? Use the following verses to help answer this question: John 1:12; Romans 10:9,10; Revelation 3:20; Ephesians 2:8,9. (After #5)

F. Discuss the following:

What is meant by **intercessory** prayer?

What is one thing that happened in your life because someone prayed for you?

(Before #9)

G. Talk about prayer lists and how each person could develop one, beginning with what he has written for question 10. Ask someone who uses a prayer list to tell how he developed it and why he likes to use it. It will be best to ask the person ahead of time to come prepared for this so that it can be well done. (Before #10)

H. Spend time in prayer for requests group members desire to share from question 10. (After #10)

I. Close by reading John 17:3 in unison three times or in three translations, and by thanking God for sending Jesus Christ.

Nehemiah's Prayer of Confession

Nehemiah 1:5-11

Let's Study It Alone With God

1. Read the entire first chapter of Nehemiah at least twice. Indicate here the number of times you read it._____ List the translations in which you read the chapter.

2. What was the situation that led to this prayer? (Verses 1-4) Observe Nehemiah's interest in his own people, the Jews, also the news he had heard about them, and how he responded to that news.

3. How did Nehemiah approach God? (By what action? by what words of address?)

4. From Nehemiah's prayer what do you discern of his concept of God?

5. Besides confession, this prayer includes adoration and petition. For each of these three aspects of prayer list one example from Nehemiah's prayer:

Adoration:

Confession:

Petition:

6. Think of your own prayers. Of which of the three aspects (adoration, confession, petition) do your prayers mostly consist? Which is the least exercised? Do you see any need for change? If so, what?

7. What two contrasting ways, in which God deals with His people, are mentioned in verses 8 and 9?

8. How are God's dealings with people related to their responses to Him? Justify your answer.

9. Notice the words, "who desire to fear the Lord," in verse 11. What does it mean to fear the Lord? (See Proverbs 8:13)

10. Read the prayer-poem at the end of the "LET'S TALK IT OVER WITH OTHERS" section. Beside as many lines or thoughts in the poem as possible, indicate, by reference, which part of Nehemiah 1 is closely related to that line or thought.

11. In addition to the prayer in chapter one, the Book of Nehemiah records other times when Nehemiah prayed. For each reference below indicate the situation in which the prayer was offered and the request that was made. (You will need to read verses before and after to determine this.) If the situation or the request is not recorded, write "not recorded." An example is given.

Reference	Situation	Request
2:4	Nehemiah was before the king to ask to go to Jerusalem.	Not recorded, but verses 5 and 6 suggest that it might have been that the king would allow him to go.
4:4,5		
4:9		

Reference	Situation	Request
5:19		
6:9		
6:14		

Reference	Situation	Request
13:14		
13:22		
13:31		

For Further Study

Indicate here questions and problems arising from this study that you would like to spend more time on later.

Let's Talk It Over With Others

To the leader: For help in using the suggestions below turn to the introductory paragraph of the **Let's Talk It Over with Others** section for the first Bible study in this book.

A. Read Psalm 119:130 and ask the Lord for understanding. (Before #1)

B. Have the group try to determine and evaluate the concept of God held by the young man in the following story:

A young man said that he was going on a trip on which he planned to do some things that he knew were wrong, and of which his church disapproved. He knew his actions would cause his parents grief. Then he added, "I know God wouldn't want me to do these things either, but when I get home I'll ask Him to forgive me and He will. Then everything will be all right." (After #4)

C. In what ways did Nehemiah show his adoration for the Lord as he prayed? What did he confess? What did he ask of God? (Have various group members share what they have written out for this part of their study. Point out that our prayers may include adoration, confession, and petition all in one prayer; or they may include only two of the three components; or sometimes only one. Help your group understand that these do not have to be in a certain order for their prayers to be acceptable to God.)(With #5)

D. How do verses 8 and 9 show that some of God's promises are not promises of blessing? How should God's promises affect the way we live? The way we pray? (After #7)

E. Have the group read Psalm 145:17-21 for insight as to how God relates to people. (After #8)

F. Point out that to fear the Lord is to respect Him, to obey Him, and to hate what He hates. Then ask these questions: How does one's fear of the Lord, or lack of it, affect the way he approaches God in prayer? what he asks of God: the amount of time he spends in prayer? (After #9)

G. Read this poem to the group, or have them read it together as a prayer.

> God, Thou art the God of heaven:
> Thou art great
> Thou art reverend
> Thou art merciful
> Thou art loving.
>
> I have wanted Thy mercy and love.
> I have seen Thee as a giver, yet
> I have not been willing to give
> Myself
> My desires
> My ambitions
> My possessions
> To Thee.
>
> I have kept these for myself.
> I have not seen Thee as one
> Who is great
> Who is reverend
> Who hates sin.
>
> Because I have not feared Thee
> I have not feared sin;
> Rather I have feared holiness.

Lord, help me to see Thee as reverend:
To see sin—my own sin—as sin;
To desire holiness.

After reading the poem allow time for comments or for silent prayer whichever seems more appropriate at the time. (After #10)

H. You may want to use #11 as a separate lesson depending upon the amount of time your group can spend in their own study and in meeting together.

Jehoshaphat's Prayer of Confidence

II Chronicles 20:1-19

Let's Study It Alone With God

1. Read the prayer three times, using one translation or several. List here the translations you used and the number of times you read each.

2. What news had Jehoshaphat received? How did he respond to this news? (vv. 1-3).

3. Locate all the places mentioned in verses 1-3 on a map. How does this help you to understand Jehoshaphat's fear mentioned in verse 3?

4. What did Jehoshaphat think the enemy countries were planning to do? (v. 11)

5. How does this prayer show confidence in God's power? List the statements Jehoshaphat made about God that show his confidence in God. (vv. 4-12)

6. What did Jehoshaphat say that shows his confidence was not in himself or in his army. (v. 12)

7. How did God answer Jehoshaphat's prayer? (vv. 14-17)

8. How did Jehoshaphat and his people respond to God's answer? (vv. 18, 19)

9. Read II Chronicles 20:20-30, filling the three sections below to show what happened after the people knew that the battle was the Lord's.

   a. What the people did:

   b. What God did:

   c. The results:

10. Note how Jehoshaphat and his people were involved in God's answer to prayer. In the space below tell about a time when God answered a prayer of yours by involving you in the answer.

11. What part of this Scripture passage is most significant to you? Why?

For Further Study

Indicate here questions and problems coming from this study that you would like to spend more time on later.

Let's Talk It Over With Others

To the leader: For help in using the suggestions below turn to the introductory paragraph of the **Let's Talk It Over with Others** section for the first study in this book.

A. Lead the group in singing the first stanza of "Great Is Thy Faithfulness." Have one member lead in prayer, thanking God for His faithfulness and asking that the group may understand more of His faithfulness through this Bible study. (Before #1)

B. Show a map that has all of the places mentioned in II Chronicles 20:1-3 on it. Point these out. (With #3)

C. Ask each of several persons to mention one of Jehoshaphat's statements that shows his confidence in God. Ask each person also to comment on the significance of the statement he mentions. (with #5)

D. How do you know that Jehoshaphat realized that he could not win the battle alone? (After #6)

E. What is the relationship between one's recognition of his own limitations and his dependence on God? (After #6)

F. What does this study show us about God's response to those who depend upon Him instead of upon themselves? (After #9)

G. Ask each member of the group to share the part of this Scripture passage most meaningful to him. (After #11)

H. Ask each one to think of a difficult situation in his life wherein he knows that unless the Lord takes over nothing can be done. If the group members desire to share these and pray for each other, do so. Otherwise ask each to pray silently for his situation. Then close the meeting in a short verbal prayer of commitment. (After #11)

Daniel's Prayer of Urgency

Daniel 9:1-19

Let's Study It Alone With God

1. How did Daniel know that God's judgment was coming to Jerusalem? (v. 2)

2. Read Jeremiah 25:8-11. What did Jeremiah say would happen to Daniel's country (Judah and Jerusalem) because the people had not listened to God?

3. What did Daniel's reading of the Scriptures lead him to do? (Dan. 9:2, 3) What does this show us about the relationship between reading the Word of God and praying?

4. How does verse 3 reflect the urgency of Daniel's prayer?

5. Read the entire prayer (vv. 9-13), noticing the ways in which Daniel acknowledged God. Copy the various expressions he used in addressing God.

6. What sins did Daniel acknowledge in this prayer?

7. What petitions did he make?

8. Reread the entire prayer. By what character qualities and actions had God revealed Himself to His people?

9. How had the people responded to God's dealings with them?

10. List all the expressions in the prayer that show Daniel's urgency in praying.

11. What kinds of experiences cause God's people today to pray with urgency?

12. Recall one of your own prayers which you consider a prayer of urgency. What situation led to it? How did God respond?

13. What is one prayer request that you consider urgent at this time?

14. What part of Daniel's prayer is the most significant to you? Why?

For Further Study

Indicate here questions and problems coming from this study that you would like to spend more time on later.

Let's Talk It Over With Others

To the leader: For help in using suggestions below turn to the introductory paragraph of the **Let's Talk It Over With Others** section for the first study in this book.

A. Ask one member of the group to lead in prayer. (Before #1)

B. Share **briefly** the background from Jeremiah 25:1-11 with the group, or have someone who has done a special assignment on it give a report. (With #2)

C. Ask if any in the group recall a time when, while reading the Bible, they were caused to stop to pray about something they were reading. Allow time for sharing experiences. (After #3)

D. Why could this prayer also be called a prayer of confession? (After #6)

E. Why could this prayer also be called a prayer of petition? (After #7)

F. Are people's responses to God today similar to those to which Daniel referred? Explain. (After #9)

G. Comment that sometimes urgent praying comes out of problems people bring upon themselves. Ask for examples. Mention also that not all urgent prayers are because of such problems. Ask for examples. (After #11)

H. Allow time for sharing requests and prayer. (After #13)

I. Ask if any selected a verse for #14 that has a note of encouragement in it. If not, share one of your own that does. Close thanking God for that encouragement. (After #14)

Hezekiah's Prayer
of Distress

II Kings 20:1-11

Let's Study It Alone With God

1. What had Isaiah told Hezekiah? (v. 1)

2. How did Hezekiah respond to Isaiah's message? (v. 2)

3. What did Hezekiah ask God to remember in dealing with him? (v. 3)

4. What was God's response to Hezekiah's prayer? (vv. 4-7)

5. Why did God answer the prayer as He did? (v. 6)

6. Describe Hezekiah's faith or lack of it in this situation? (vv. 7-10)

7. How did God respond to Hezekiah? (vv. 9-11)

8. In what ways did God use a person in dealing with Hezekiah in this situation? (vv. 1, 7-11)

9. Recall a time when God used a person in connection with an answer to your prayer. Describe.

Note: Questions 1-9 are on the prayer. The following questions are on the person who prayed. Do a study of Hezekiah as a person. You may limit this study to the time from Hezekiah's illness to his death (II Kings 20:1-21 and II Chronicles 32:24-33), or you may extend the study and begin at the time Hezekiah became king of Judah (II Kings 18-20 and II Chronicles 29-32). In either case, you will find several answers to each question below. It will be well to give the reference for each point you make. This will be helpful in relocating it later. One illustration is given for each question.

10. What were Hezekiah's strengths?

He believed God's promise to deliver his people from the king of Assyria (II Chron. 32:11; cf. II Kings 20:6)

11. What were his weaknesses?

Times of pride crept in (II Chron. 32:25)

12. What was his attitude toward God?

    God is the only true God. Hezekiah took away other places of worship. (II Chron. 32:12)

13. What was his attitude toward himself?

    He said that he had followed God with a perfect heart. (II Kings 20:3)

14. How did he relate to other people?

    When Sennacherib defied God, Hezekiah prayed (II Chron. 32:17-20)

15. How did he relate to his circumstances and responsibilities?

    When he was advised that his people should keep the passover, something they had not been doing, he sent word to all the people that they should come and observe it. (II Chron. 30:1-6)

16. What were the results of the way he lived?

    He prospered. (II Chron. 31:21)

17. What example(s) in his life would be good for you to follow?

    To do everything for the Lord wholeheartedly (II Chron. 31:20)

18. What weaknesses in his life should you seek to avoid?

    His lack of discernment in the way he responded to personal attention (II Kings 20:12-17)

19. Other observations:

    Hezekiah had worked with all his heart to establish religious reforms in Judah, and the people had responded. There was spiritual victory. After that, the king of Assyria, a God-defying man, threatened to take the land (II Chron. 31:2-32:8; esp. 31:21 and 32:1). How true to life! —after the spiritual victory comes the test of putting it into practice in real-life battles right down here on earth.

For Further Study

Indicate here questions and problems coming from this study that you would like to spend more time on later.

Let's Talk It Over With Others

To the leader: For help in using the suggestions below turn to the introductory paragraph of the **Let's Talk It Over With Others** section for the first study in this book.

A. Open the session with prayer and/or suggest a hymn about prayer for the group to sing. (Before #1)

B. How do situations of distress affect a person's prayer life? Evaluate. (After #2)

C. Ask for illustrations of times of distress when they experienced a mixture of faith and doubts. (After #6)

D. Note Isaiah's part in this account. What does this tell us about God's use of people to accomplish His purpose in our lives? (After #8)

E. Ask members of the group to volunteer to share times when God used a person in their lives as He answered their prayer. Determine various ways God uses one person to answer another's prayers. (With #9)

F. Refer back to verse one. Ask what it would mean for us to "set our house in order" if we knew that our lives would end soon. What would we need to do? (After #9)

G. Have each person share the thought from this study that was most meaningful to him. These may come from one's own study, from the discussion, or from an application one has already made. (After #9)

H. You may want to make a separate study of the section on Hezekiah himself. If so, make that an assignment and then close in prayer after #9. Otherwise proceed through questions 10-19.

The Publican's Prayer of Humility

Luke 18:9-14

Let's Study It Alone With God

1. To whom did Jesus tell this story?

2. What did the Pharisee say that he was thankful for?

3. How does the Pharisee's prayer reflect what he thought of other people? Of himself?

4. How does the publican's (tax-collector's) prayer reflect his opinion of himself?

5. What did Jesus say would be the effect of the attitudes of these men?

6. Reread the passage to determine why Jesus told this particular story to the people to whom He told it.

7. Think of an illustration of how pride can affect the way a person prays. Describe.

8. Think of an illustration of how humility can affect the way a person prays. Describe.

9. Find illustrations of humility in the Bible by going back over all the prayers studied in this unit to note the element of humility in them. Copy a statement or summarize a thought that shows humility in each one.

Paul's Prayer of Petition: Ephesians 3:13-21

David's Prayer of Thanksgiving: I Chronicles 29:10-19

Jesus' Prayer of Intercession: John 17

Nehemiah's Prayer of Confession: Nehemiah 1:5-11

Jehoshaphat's Prayer of Confidence: II Chronicles 20:1-19

Daniel's Prayer of Urgency: Daniel 9:1-19

Hezekiah's Prayer of Distress: II Kings 20:1-11

The Publican's Prayer of Humility: Luke 18:9-14

For Further Study

Indicate here questions and problems coming from this study that you would like to spend more time on later.

Let's Talk It Over With Others

To the leader: For help in using the suggestions below turn to the introductory paragraph of the **Let's Talk It Over With Others** section for the first study of this book.

A. Open the session with prayer, either silently or by having one in the group pray aloud. (Before #1)

B. Have the group read the passage in unison if they all have the same translation of the Bible; otherwise have one person read it aloud to the group. (Before #1)

C. To whom was the Pharisee really praying? Do you think it is possible for some people to think they are praying to God when they really are not? If so, give illustrations. (After #3)

D. How do people's prayers reflect their attitude toward themselves? Toward others? Toward God? (After #3)

E. Ask group members to share the illustrations they have as to how pride can affect the way a person prays. Ask also for the illustrations of the way humility can affect a person's praying. Point out contrasts as to how pride and humility affect the way a person prays. (With #7 and #8)

F. Why did Jesus tell this story to the people to whom He told it? (After #8)

G. Imagine the group to whom Jesus told this story. What are some possible ways in which individuals in that group could have responded to that story? (After #8)

H. Assign each person in the group one of the prayers studied in this unit. Then give them time to go over the Scripture passage and/or their notes to find an illustration of humility in that prayer. Share these. (With #9)

I. Close by summarizing God's response to man's humility, and by reading together Psalm 10:17.

unit two

This unit is made up of four prayers. Each study is based on eleven parts, most of these parts being questions.

The study guides for these four prayers are all alike. the questions and other aspects of the guide have been gleaned from the forms used for the study of the eight prayers in Unit One. It is a guide that can be used for many other prayers besides those used in Unit Two.

It is often the case that persons with little background or insufficient interest in Bible study use a simple guide very sketchily. Others who have the background and interest can take the same guide and do a rich depth-study of the passage. Persons who have done the studies in Unit One should be able to use the guide in Unit Two very effectively because they will be familiar with the questions and they will also make some observations that are beyond the specifics asked for in this particular guide.

On each of the four copies of the guide, the passage of Scripture is filled in. This will direct the person to the record of the prayer to be considered. The rest of the study is entirely up to the person. This causes him to search for himself what the Scriptures say and to experience for himself the joy of seeing what God has given him.

In general the instructions given at the beginning of Unit One will apply to this unit also. The discussion time should be based on the eleven parts in the guide, though they need not be referred to in that order. Sometimes the group may want to begin by discussing the attitude toward God which is reflected in the prayer, especially if that prayer shows an attitude concurrent with or in direct opposition to an attitude current in the daily news. Sometimes the group may want to spend some of their time in prayer, especially if several have requests based on the study at hand, If everyone is prepared and seems enthusiastic about a study, it might be well to begin that time by letting everyone tell which part of the prayer impressed him most. This may well be the main part of that discussion time together, for as each shares his part he will probably deal with one part of the study guide while another concentrates on a different part. The leader should be alert to this in order to aYoid too much overlap and also to be sure that there are no important omissions.

After this unit is completed, members should be encouraged to refer to this study guide whenever they come upon a prayer in the Bible. Perhaps some of them will want to select other prayers in the Bible and continue a similar study on their own.

Studies in this Unit

I Samuel 1
I Kings 3
Genesis 24
Jeremiah 32

None of the passages above consists of only prayer; however, the entire chapter is included in order that one may see the setting of the prayer, the prayer itself, and such things as God's response to the prayer and the effect that it had on the person who made it.

Do not force an answer for every part of the study guide. For instance, one prayer may have no confession in it and another may have no record of its effect on the life of the person who prayed it. This is a guide that can be used to study many prayers in the Bible, but this does not imply that each prayer to be studied includes every aspect of prayer considered in the guide.

Guide For Studying
A Prayer
I Samuel 1

1. Who prayed this prayer?

2. What was the occasion of the prayer?

3. What requests were made in the prayer?

4. What aspects of prayer besides that of requests are included: Check those that are included. Then give an example of each.

____Adoration

____Confession

____Thanksgiving

____Commitment or promise to God

5. What kind of attitude toward God is reflected in this prayer?

6. Is there a record of God's response to the prayer? If so, what was His response?

7. Is there a record of how this prayer affected people's lives later on? (The person who prayed the prayer? Others?) If so, how?

8. What examples are there for your own prayer life? Use the following questions to develop this.

   a. What one thing from this prayer could you pray for another person?

   b. What one thing from this prayer could you pray for yourself?

   c. What one thing from this prayer would you like for another person to pray for you?

   d. What part of the prayer impresses you most? Why?

9. Consider the person who prayed this prayer. Write out observations you make as to any of the following which are reflected in the passage.

a. His attitude toward God

b. His attitude toward himself

c. His attitude toward other people

d. His attitude toward responsibilities and circumstances

10. Go back over the entire study and choose one thing that you would like to see effective in your life. Summarize your thoughts here, including any action you can take in order to realize this potential in your life.

11. Use this space for other observations on the passage or for notes you want to add when you discuss this study with someone else.

Guide For Studying
A Prayer
I Kings 3

1. Who prayed this prayer?

2. What was the occasion of the prayer?

3. What requests were made in the prayer?

4. What aspects of prayer besides that of requests are included: Check those that are included. Then give an example of each.

____Adoration

____Confession

____Thanksgiving

____Commitment or promise to God

5. What kind of attitude toward God is reflected in this prayer?

6. Is there a record of God's response to the prayer? If so, what was His response?

7. Is there a record of how this prayer affected people's lives later on? (The person who prayed the prayer? Others?) If so, how?

8. What examples are there for your own prayer life? Use the following questions to develop this.

   a. What one thing from this prayer could you pray for another person?

   b. What one thing from this prayer could you pray for yourself?

   c. What one thing from this prayer would you like for another person to pray for you?

   d. What part of the prayer impresses you most? Why?

9. Consider the person who prayed this prayer. Write out observations you make as to any of the following which are reflected in the passage.

a. His attitude toward God

b. His attitude toward himself

c. His attitude toward other people

d. His attitude toward responsibilities and circumstances

10. Go back over the entire study and choose one thing that you would like to see effective in your life. Summarize your thoughts here, including any action you can take in order to realize this potential in your life.

11. Use this space for other observations on the passage or for notes you want to add when you discuss this study with someone else.

Guide For Studying
A Prayer
Genesis 24

1. Who prayed this prayer?

2. What was the occasion of the prayer?

3. What requests were made in the prayer?

4. What aspects of prayer beside that of requests are included: Check those that are included. Then give an example of each.

____Adoration

____Confession

____Thanksgiving

____Commitment or promise to God

5. What kind of attitude toward God is reflected in this prayer?

6. Is there a record of God's response to the prayer? If so, what was His response?

7. Is there a record of how this prayer affected people's lives later on? (The person who prayed the prayer? Others?) If so, how?

8. What examples are there for your own prayer life? Use the following questions to develop this.

   a. What one thing from this prayer could you pray for another person?

   b. What one thing from this prayer could you pray for yourself?

   c. What one thing from this prayer would you like for another person to pray for you?

   d. What part of the prayer impresses you most? Why?

9. Consider the person who prayed this prayer. Write out observations you make as to any of the following which are reflected in the passage.

a. His attitude toward God

b. His attitude toward himself

c. His attitude toward other people

d. His attitude toward responsibilities and circumstances

10. Go back over the entire study and choose one thing that you would like to see effective in your life. Summarize your thoughts here, including any action you can take in order to realize this potential in your life.

11. Use this space for other observations on the passage or for notes you want to add when you discuss this study with someone else.

Guide For Studying
A Prayer
Jeremiah 32

1. Who prayed this prayer?

2. What was the occasion of the prayer?

3. What requests were made in the prayer?

4. What aspects of prayer besides that of requests are included: Check those that are included. Then give an example of each.

____Adoration

____Confession

____Thanksgiving

____Commitment or promise to God

5. What kind of attitude toward God is reflected in this prayer?

6. Is there a record of God's response to the prayer? If so, what was His response?

7. Is there a record of how this prayer affected people's lives later on? (The person who prayed the prayer? Others?) If so, how?

8. What examples are there for your own prayer life? Use the following questions to develop this.

   a. What one thing from this prayer could you pray for another person?

   b. What one thing from this prayer could you pray for yourself?

   c. What one thing from this prayer would you like for another person to pray for you?

   d. What part of the prayer impresses you most? Why?

9. Consider the person who prayed this prayer. Write out observations you make as to any of the following which are reflected in the passage.

a. His attitude toward God

b. His attitude toward himself

c. His attitude toward other people

d. His attitude toward responsibilities and circumstances

10. Go back over the entire study and choose one thing that you would like to see effective in your life. Summarize your thoughts here, including any action you can take in order to realize this potential in your life.

11. Use this space for other observations on the passage or for notes you want to add when you discuss this study with someone else.

on your own

If individuals in the group or the group as a whole wants to continue the study of Bible prayers, the following prayers could be studied. The same guide as used for Unit Two will work well here. Each prayer should be studied in context so that one understand the occasion that led to the prayer and the results of it.

The Prayer of Paul . . . . Ephesians 1:15-23
The Prayer of Paul . . . . Philippians 1:3-11
The Prayer of the early believers . . . . Acts 12:5-19
The Prayer of Elijah. . . . . I Kings 18:25-41
The Prayer of David . . . . II Samuel 7:18-29
The Prayer of David . . . . Psalm 51
The Prayer of Joshua . . . . Joshua 7:6-15

Following is a supply of study guides for use with the above prayers and/or others you come across as you read your Bible.

Guide For Studying
A Prayer

Scripture Passage_____

1. Who prayed this prayer?

2. What was the occasion of the prayer?

3. What requests were made in the prayer?

4. What aspect of prayer besides that of requests are included: Check those that are included. Then give an example of each.

____Adoration

____Confession

____Thanksgiving

____Commitment or promise to God

5. What kind of attitude toward God is reflected in this prayer?

6. Is there a record of God's response to the prayer? If so, what was His response?

7. Is there a record of how this prayer affected people's lives later on? (The person who prayed the prayer? Others?) If so, how?

8. What examples are there for your own prayer life? Use the following questions to develop this.

   a. What one thing from this prayer could you pray for another person?

   b. What one thing from this prayer could you pray for yourself?

   c. What one thing from this prayer would you like for another person to pray for you?

   d. What part of the prayer impresses you most? Why?

9. Consider the person who prayed this prayer. Write out observations you make as to any of the following which are reflected in the passage.

a. His attitude toward God

b. His attitude toward himself

c. His attitude toward other people

d. His attitude toward responsibilities and circumstances

10. Go back over the entire study and choose one thing that you would like to see effective in your life. Summarize your thoughts here, including any action you can take in order to realize this potential in your life.

11. Use this space for other observations on the passage or for notes you want to add when you discuss this study with someone else.

Guide For Studying
A Prayer

Scripture Passage_____

1. Who prayed this prayer?

2. What was the occasion of the prayer?

3. What requests were made in the prayer?

4. What aspects of prayer besides that of requests are included: Check those that are included. Then give an example of each.

    ____Adoration

    ____Confession

    ____Thanksgiving

    ____Commitment or promise to God

5. What kind of attitude toward God is reflected in this prayer?

6. Is there a record of God's response to the prayer? If so, what was His response?

7. Is there a record of how this prayer affected people's lives later on? (The person who prayed the prayer? Others?) If so, how?

8. What examples are there for your own prayer life? Use the following questions to develop this.

   a. What one thing from this prayer could you pray for another person?

   b. What one thing from this prayer could you pray for yourself?

   c. What one thing from this prayer would you like for another person to pray for you?

   d. What part of the prayer impresses you most? Why?

9. Consider the person who prayed this prayer. Write out observations you make as to any of the following which are reflected in the passage.

a. His attitude toward God

b. His attitude toward himself

c. His attitude toward other people

d. His attitude toward responsibilities and circumstances

10. Go back over the entire study and choose one thing that you would like to see effective in your life. Summarize your thoughts here, including any action you can take in order to realize this potential in your life.

11. Use this space for other observations on the passage or for notes you want to add when you discuss this study with someone else.

Guide For Studying
A Prayer

Scripture Passage_____

1. Who prayed this prayer?

2. What was the occasion of the prayer?

3. What requests were made in the prayer?

4. What aspects of prayer besides that of requests are included: Check those that are included. Then give an example of each.

____Adoration

____Confession

____Thanksgiving

____Commitment or promise to God

5. What kind of attitude toward God is reflected in this prayer?

6. Is there a record of God's response to the prayer? If so, what was His response?

7. Is there a record of how this prayer affected people's lives later on? (The person who prayed the prayer? Others?) If so, how?

8. What examples are there for your own prayer life? Use the following questions to develop this.

   a. What one thing from this prayer could you pray for another person?

   b. What one thing from this prayer could you pray for yourself?

   c. What one thing from this prayer would you like for another person to pray for you?

   d. What part of the prayer impresses you most? Why?

9. Consider the person who prayed this prayer. Write out observations you make as to any of the following which are reflected in the passage.

a. His attitude toward God

b. His attitude toward himself

c. His attitude toward other people

d. His attitude toward responsibilities and circumstances

10. Go back over the entire study and choose one thing that you would like to see effective in your life. Summarize your thoughts here, including any action you can take in order to realize this potential in your life.

11. Use this space for other observations on the passage or for notes you want to add when you discuss this study with someone else.

Guide For Studying
A Prayer

Scripture Passage_____

1. Who prayed this prayer?

2. What was the occasion of the prayer?

3. What requests were made in the prayer?

4. What aspects of prayer besides that of requests are included: Check those that are included. Then give an example of each.

____Adoration

____Confession

____Thanksgiving

____Commitment or promise to God

5. What kind of attitude toward God is reflected in this prayer?

6. Is there a record of God's response to the prayer? If so, what was His response?

7. Is there a record of how this prayer affected people's lives later on? (The person who prayed the prayer? Others?) If so, how?

8. What examples are there for your own prayer life? Use the following questions to develop this.

   a. What one thing from this prayer could you pray for another person?

   b. What one thing from this prayer could you pray for yourself?

   c. What one thing from this prayer would you like for another person to pray for you?

   d. What part of the prayer impresses you most? Why?

9. Consider the person who prayed this prayer. Write out observations you make as to any of the following which are reflected in the passage.

a. His attitude toward God

b. His attitude toward himself

c. His attitude toward other people

d. His attitude toward responsibilities and circumstances

10. Go back over the entire study and choose one thing that you would like to see effective in your life. Summarize your thoughts here, including any action you can take in order to realize this potential in your life.

11. Use this space for other observations on the passage or for notes you want to add when you discuss this study with someone else.

Guide For Studying
A Prayer

Scripture Passage_____

1. Who prayed this prayer?

2. What was the occasion of the prayer?

3. What requests were made in the prayer?

4. What aspects of prayer besides that of requests are included: Check those that are included. Then give an example of each.

____Adoration

____Confession

____Thanksgiving

____Commitment or promise to God

Guide For Studying
A Prayer

Scripture Passage_____

1. Who prayed this prayer?

2. What was the occasion of the prayer?

3. What requests were made in the prayer?

4. What aspects of prayer besides that of requests are included: Check those that are included. Then give an example of each.

   ____Adoration

   ____Confession

   ____Thanksgiving

   ____Commitment or promise to God

5. What kind of attitude toward God is reflected in this prayer?

6. Is there a record of God's response to the prayer? If so, what was His response?

7. Is there a record of how this prayer affected people's lives later on? (The person who prayed the prayer? Others?) If so, how?

8. What examples are there for your own prayer life? Use the following questions to develop this.

   a. What one thing from this prayer could you pray for another person?

   b. What one thing from this prayer could you pray for yourself?

   c. What one thing from this prayer would you like for another person to pray for you?

   d. What part of the prayer impresses you most? Why?

9. Consider the person who prayed this prayer. Write out observations you make as to any of the following which are reflected in the passage.

a. His attitude toward God

b. His attitude toward himself

c. His attitude toward other people

d. His attitude toward responsibilities and circumstances

10. Go back over the entire study and choose one thing that you would like to see effective in your life. Summarize your thoughts here, including any action you can take in order to realize this potential in your life.

11. Use this space for other observations on the passage or for notes you want to add when you discuss this study with someone else.

Guide For Studying
A Prayer

Scripture Passage_____

1. Who prayed this prayer?

2. What was the occasion of the prayer?

3. What requests were made in the prayer?

4. What aspects of prayer besides that of requests are included: Check those that are included. Then give an example of each.

____Adoration

____Confession

____Thanksgiving

____Commitment or promise to God

5. What kind of attitude toward God is reflected in this prayer?

6. Is there a record of God's response to the prayer? If so, what was His response?

7. Is there a record of how this prayer affected people's lives later on? (The person who prayed the prayer? Others?) If so, how?

8. What examples are there for your own prayer life? Use the following questions to develop this.

    a. What one thing from this prayer could you pray for another person?

    b. What one thing from this prayer could you pray for yourself?

    c. What one thing from this prayer would you like for another person to pray for you?

    d. What part of the prayer impresses you most? Why?

9. Consider the person who prayed this prayer. Write out observations you make as to any of the following which are reflected in the passage.

a. His attitude toward God

b. His attitude toward himself

c. His attitude toward other people

d. His attitude toward responsibilities and circumstances

10. Go back over the entire study and choose one thing that you would like to see effective in your life. Summarize your thoughts here, including any action you can take in order to realize this potential in your life.

11. Use this space for other observations on the passage or for notes you want to add when you discuss this study with someone else.

Guide For Studying A Prayer

Scripture Passage_____

1. Who prayed this prayer?

2. What was the occasion of the prayer?

3. What requests were made in the prayer?

4. What aspects of prayer besides that of requests are included: Check those that are included. Then give an example of each.

_____Adoration

_____Confession

_____Thanksgiving

_____Commitment or promise to God

5. What kind of attitude toward God is reflected in this prayer?

6. Is there a record of God's response to the prayer? If so, what was His response?

7. Is there a record of how this prayer affected people's lives later on? (The person who prayed the prayer? Others?) If so, how?

8. What examples are there for your own prayer life? Use the following questions to develop this.

   a. What one thing from this prayer could you pray for another person?

   b. What one thing from this prayer could you pray for yourself?

   c. What one thing from this prayer would you like for another person to pray for you?

   d. What part of the prayer impresses you most? Why?

9. Consider the person who prayed this prayer. Write out observations you make as to any of the following which are reflected in the passage.

a. His attitude toward God

b. His attitude toward himself

c. His attitude toward other people

d. His attitude toward responsibilities and circumstances

10. Go back over the entire study and choose one thing that you would like to see effective in your life. Summarize your thoughts here, including any action you can take in order to realize this potential in your life.

11. Use this space for other observations on the passage or for notes you want to add when you discuss this study with someone else.

Guide For Studying
A Prayer

Scripture Passage_____

1. Who prayed this prayer?

2. What was the occasion of the prayer?

3. What requests were made in the prayer?

4. What aspects of prayer besides that of requests are included:
   Check those that are included. Then give an example of
   each.

   ____Adoration

   ____Confession

   ____Thanksgiving

   ____Commitment or promise to God

5. What kind of attitude toward God is reflected in this prayer?

6. Is there a record of God's response to the prayer? If so, what was His response?

7. Is there a record of how this prayer affected people's lives later on? (The person who prayed the prayer? Others?) If so, how?

8. What examples are there for your own prayer life? Use the following questions to develop this.

   a. What one thing from this prayer could you pray for another person?

   b. What one thing from this prayer could you pray for yourself?

   c. What one thing from this prayer would you like for another person to pray for you?

   d. What part of the prayer impresses you most? Why?

9. Consider the person who prayed this prayer. Write out observations you make as to any of the following which are reflected in the passage.

a. His attitude toward God

b. His attitude toward himself

c. His attitude toward other people

d. His attitude toward responsibilities and circumstances

10. Go back over the entire study and choose one thing that you would like to see effective in your life. Summarize your thoughts here, including any action you can take in order to realize this potential in your life.

11. Use this space for other observations on the passage or for notes you want to add when you discuss this study with someone else.

Guide For Studying
A Prayer

Scripture Passage_____

1. Who prayed this prayer?

2. What was the occasion of the prayer?

3. What requests were made in the prayer?

4. What aspects of prayer besides that of requests are included: Check those that are included. Then give an example of each.

____Adoration

____Confession

____Thanksgiving

____Commitment or promise to God

5. What kind of attitude toward God is reflected in this prayer?

6. Is there a record of God's response to the prayer? If so, what was His response?

7. Is there a record of how this prayer affected people's lives later on? (The person who prayed the prayer? Others?) If so, how?

8. What examples are there for your own prayer life? Use the following questions to develop this.

   a. What one thing from this prayer could you pray for another person?

   b. What one thing from this prayer could you pray for yourself?

   c. What one thing from this prayer would you like for another person to pray for you?

   d. What part of the prayer impresses you most? Why?

9. Consider the person who prayed this prayer. Write out observations you make as to any of the following which are reflected in the passage.

a. His attitude toward God

b. His attitude toward himself

c. His attitude toward other people

d. His attitude toward responsibilities and circumstances

10. Go back over the entire study and choose one thing that you would like to see effective in your life. Summarize your thoughts here, including any action you can take in order to realize this potential in your life.

11. Use this space for other observations on the passage or for notes you want to add when you discuss this study with someone else.